M000315752

by all means
A ZEN CAUTIONARY TALE

words Edward Brown
drawings Margot Koch
painting John Simpkins

MISSING LINKS PRESS

Copyright © 2013 by Edward Brown
Drawings Copyright © 2013 Margot Koch
Painting Copyright © 2013 John Simpkins
All rights reserved.
Published by Missing Links Press
San Francisco, California
www.missinglinkspress.com

Paperbound: ISBN 978-0-9899228-0-7
Clothbound: ISBN 978-0-9899228-1-4

No part of this publication may be reproduced, stored in
a retrieval system, or transmitted — in any form or by any
means, electronic, mechanical, photocopying, recording, or
otherwise — without written permission from the publisher.

Cover and interior design:
Ingalls Design, San Francisco

First Printing, January 2014

by all means
is dedicated
to grown-ups
of all ages

"Realizing the mystery,"
says Zen Master Deshan,
"is nothing but breaking
through to grasp an
ordinary person's life."

Who do you think you are?

by all means

Chapter One

Lying on top of the cherry red comforter with its design of purple leaves, I hold Ponce tenderly on my chest. I'm not sure if Ponce notices the love that I extend to him—after all, he is a black pig hand puppet with white forefeet and a white stripe circling his upper body, along with a light caramel nose, inner ears and a fine fat curly piggy tail—but I can feel his wound that he tries so carefully to conceal. As soon as I extend my heart to do so, I can touch his little piggy pain. That's as big as the whole world. Ponce's feeling three years old and his mommy's died, leaving a huge hole inside.

It's terribly confusing too, because he loved her so much, so completely, and he cannot for the life of him figure out what he did wrong that would make her leave and not come back, but whatever it was he'd better be really careful not to do it again.

All the hugs in the world will not bring her back, nor will Ponce's puzzling about what to do.

Chapter Two

It may be that Ponce's nose, inner ear, and tail are not really the color of light caramel—that probably makes Ponce sound sweeter than he is. But if you said that these specially sensitive Ponce parts were oatmeal, that would make Ponce sound more drab than he is, as he is a bit more dashing than oatmeal—both in terms of color and of character.

Ponce could remember times when people ate oatmeal, back in the old days before business got around to making people superfluous by manufacturing breakfast cereals and putting them in boxes.

Aside from being astonishingly good consumers (if they have the money), what are people for?

Chapter Three

In just the few days that I had known him Ponce and I had become the best of friends. It may be that Ponce's little piggy pain was really my own gaping wound that hurt so much that sharing it with anyone was problematic. Still Ponce was willing to let me share *my* big pain with *him*, while I pretended that it was his—and as long as I was pretending I really believed that it was Ponce's pain. Ponce was a real friend in that regard, because not every critter you meet can stomach such a blend of fact, fantasy, and fiction without trying to sort out which was which, which was whose, and how to fix it for the better.

The gift Ponce gave was simply to take it all in, as though he had that gift to give. To take it all in without protest or shaming, without feeling attacked or belittled. "Yes," was all he said, in his silent way, "yes, that's a big pain we have here, and we're fast friends aren't we—inseparable."

Fast friends indeed, seemingly life-long, after just a few days of drama together.

Chapter Four

Ponce's life had changed dramatically just a week or two earlier. He'd been on the shelf for many months—by all means a nice enough shelf at the top of a bookcase with a grand view of the whole room where people who were not very interested in Ponce came and went. *Not very interested* indeed, they took absolutely no notice *at all* of Ponce, who decided in the absence of social contact to cultivate his meditation skills.

He focused on his breathing, the sensations of inhalation and exhalation, which were quite subtle, and soon enough, sure enough, he could not tell the difference between deep meditation and being completely spaced out.

Which was he? How were you supposed to know?

Chapter Five

Still nobody noticed that he was a good little pig, a prize pig, giving his heart to all beings from his shelf at the top of the bookcase. Then one day something furry leapt onto the shelf and knocked Ponce onto the floor. Ponce had no idea what was happening, as the white and black creature tried to bite into his neck, which was not taking very well to the idea. Then rather rudely Ponce was being bounced and prodded, pushed and shoved out the door of the bedroom and down the hallway with its wooden floor, through the office with its green carpet, fruit dehydrator, books, and papers.

Ponce was having trouble digesting the situation, not knowing if it was an adventure or a mis-adventure. Yes, he had been noticed and someone was taking an interest in him. Still, he had no say in the matter, and though he did want to do what others wanted if it would make them happy, he didn't want to be stupid about it. On they went, Ponce being rolled across the linoleum floor of the kitchen, past the wine bottles and used brown bags in their wire basket, and down the grey-carpeted back steps. Ponce was encountering the neighbor's cat, incongruously named Turtle, a wildly curious beast who apparently had a stuffed animal fetish, as tales were told about his prowling the neighborhood looking for stuffies to carry off as his prey.

Across the dusty and dirty cement floor of the laundry room, past the white front-loading washer and past the rebuilt cream-colored drier. Now at the back door the light from outside was dazzling.

Ponce's heart leapt and despaired simultaneously.

What would happen next?

Chapter Six

Ponce had never been very good at establishing boundaries. He was pretty small and didn't really know how to stand up for himself. People and other critters just treated you the way they did, and Ponce had no say in the matter. He hadn't really found his voice—the one that could say, "no." All he had was a plastic squeaker on top of his head, and it always said, "yes... yes," when someone pressed him there, and sometimes they didn't just press. They bopped him over the head pretty hard, and all he could say was, "Yes." Squeak! Squeak! It was like an invitation: Do what you want with me, because all I know is how to say "Yes."

Wasn't that how you got people to love you?

Chapter Seven

Ponce's heart had leapt at seeing the sunlight, as it meant a possible adventure in the light of day, but at the same time the neighbor cat was toying with him, arching back, and then leaping on him anew. Slowly but surely he was being wrestled out the door, and it didn't seem as though anyone was considering his wishes in the matter, and truth be told Ponce, was so confused and disoriented that he did not know what his own wishes were.

How were you supposed to know these things?

Chapter Eight

Now an even larger creature appeared. Busy doing grown-up things out in the yard, he had spotted the cat at his back door, pawing away at an anonymous unidentifiable object. The anonymous unidentifiable object turned out to be Ponce! -who was still trying to keep his wits about him—and at the time didn't even know that he was "Ponce." Life was very confusing! The big person wanted to find out what was going on at his back door. Realizing that a stuffed animal was at risk, he snatched Ponce away from the cat, shooed the cat away from the house, and stared at Ponce befuddled. He didn't know if the cat had been stealing Ponce away, or proudly depositing his prey at the door. He'd never met Ponce before.

Was this small stuffed piggie coming or going?
That remained to be seen.

Chapter Nine

The even larger creature that had appeared was I, also known as Edward. When he was a very little boy, his mommy and daddy had called him "Edward Bear," after a character in *Winnie the Pooh*. When they felt especially loving and happy with him, they called him eddiebear. Not only did they shorten the first part of the name, but the whole name became one word: "eddiebear." Often when they used this name, it was not even capitalized. Even though it was not written down, you could still tell eddiebear was not someone proper and formal and distant, but someone close, closer than close, someone absolutely adorable. This eddiebear person was obviously someone entirely lovable — entirely! Everybody knew that! And it was the happiest thing in the whole wide world to be seen as eddiebear. Only sometimes this entirely lovable little boy disappeared, and in his place was: "Ed-ward Bear! What's going on here? You're making such a mess, and such a racket, and you are not behaving very well at all. Not at all. You'll need to learn to behave much better, young man."

Poor eddiebear found it very confusing to be suddenly invisible, and have Edward Bear take his place. eddiebear was no where to be seen. Where was the entirely lovable little boy? Why couldn't anyone see him?

Chapter Ten

This only continued as the little boy grew up to be a bigger boy and then a young man, a middle-aged man, and after a while an older man. Time had a way of continuing to happen, and you could tell it was happening even though you couldn't see it because when you looked in the mirror you didn't look the same as you did before, and if you looked at old photographs of yourself, that wasn't you at all, but some younger person or even a baby that others claimed was you, and who surely had been a nice enough creature in his way, but could hardly be said to be whom you felt you were from the inside. Besides, photographs were not going to be able to convey to people what a sweetheart you were, what a sweetheart you had always been, forever. Photographs were not going to be able to picture "eddiebear" so that others could see him plain and simple, clear as day.

People today said things like, "*You* have problems!" and "Don't talk to me like that. You're such a bad communicator." "You're way too critical and judgmental." While inside he was still eddiebear, it was pretty obvious they weren't seeing eddiebear or speaking to eddiebear. They seemed to think that he needed to be different and better than he appeared to be.

Maybe he had never been eddiebear, maybe it had all been a dream, and he had made it all up. Maybe some big person had gotten hold of his precious eddiebear body and taken over. And eddiebear had been left for dead somewhere at some other time.

How did these things work?

Chapter Eleven

Ponce lay resting on his side on top of the drier where the big
critter had left him when he took Ponce away from the furry
cat with the funny name of Turtle. It was rather dark in the
laundry room with the door closed to the brilliant light of
day. The drier was smooth and hard, and even though Ponce
lay on his side rather than sitting up straight, he started
going back to his meditation practice. Only he was really
stressed and anxious about what might have happened if it
had happened in some other way than it all had happened.
He could have been abducted from his home! In the darkness he could imagine all kinds of painful ways that the life
of Ponce could have come to an end, and how he might have
suffered if he hadn't been saved.

None of the painful things had actually happened, but the
small stuffed piggy found himself trembling in his small
stuffed piggy way because he could imagine ever so clearly so
many ways that his life of benefiting others might have been
terminated: mangled, mutilated, torn, shredded—there were
way too many possibilities, and then he began to worry that
his being safe on his side on top of the drier was yet another
way of being lost rather than found. He wouldn't be able to
help people while he was stuffed away in the darkness.

Where was his true home, where he could love and be loved?
And not be stuffed away from being seen and appreciated for
who he truly was. Trying to figure this out made his little
piggy head spin. Even though he was on top of the drier and
not inside of it whirling around.

Chapter Twelve

After awhile the big person Edward opened the door to the outside and came in from the garden patio where he had been doing some important garden work like dead-heading the daisies or tying up the dahlias that when left to their own devices preferred falling over onto the ground rather than standing up for themselves. A lot of things that Edward did were very important because it was important to him to be doing important things and not just wasting his time. Otherwise how could he have any respect for himself? And wasn't it important to be self-respecting? Because if you left it to the others, there didn't seem to be a lot of respect going around, and you weren't likely to get much.

Respect was something that had to be earned, and since Edward believed in being self-employed and self-sufficient, he found it more straight-forward and economical to earn it for himself and give it to himself, only sometimes the person giving out the respect seemed rather hard to please, and the Edward who was busy doing important things would become discouraged and wonder if maybe he was in the wrong line of work for the wrong employer.

When was enough important thing doing enough important thing doing to earn respect, and allow someone to relax a little without feeling as useless as a stuffed piggy who just sat there looking adorable?

Chapter Thirteen

The big person Edward was an older man now, for better or worse, and since he had turned sixty, he had been wondering what to do with *the time that was left*. With all the uncertainties of having a life, Edward didn't know how much time that was that was left, but it seemed that he should probably be finding something important to be doing during that time as there was less and less of it each day. He really wanted to be doing something that was engaging for himself and if at all possible enlightening for others. Enlightening others seemed like quite an important thing to be doing, as he suspected that their being enlightened meant that they would be less likely to be driven by their greed, hate, and delusion to bad vacation spots and more likely to take the wheel themselves and aim for genuine connection with their own hearts and the hearts of others.

Unfortunately enlightening others was not as straightforward as house painting or gardening, which you could actually do and get done. For one thing the others mostly were not especially interested in waking up, as they busily pursued their dreams of earning a living and having suitable entertainment *on-demand,* rather than tending to relationships in ways that would make them more workable. Oh well.

"Happiness," some proudly proclaimed, "is never having to relate with anything."

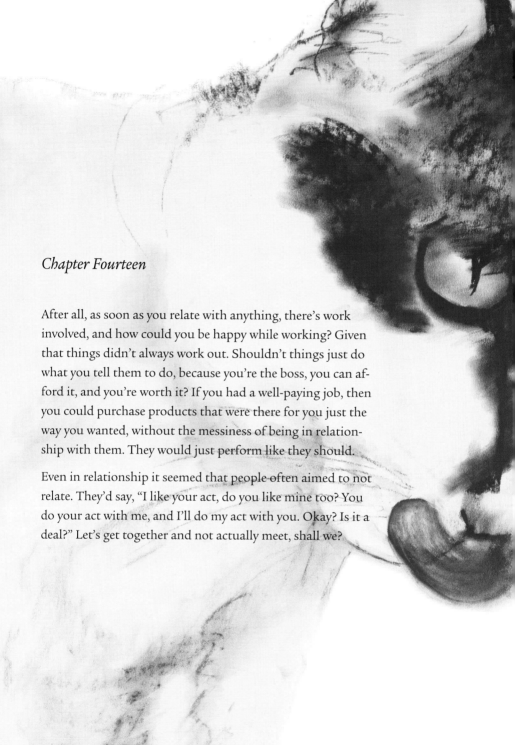

Chapter Fourteen

After all, as soon as you relate with anything, there's work involved, and how could you be happy while working? Given that things didn't always work out. Shouldn't things just do what you tell them to do, because you're the boss, you can afford it, and you're worth it? If you had a well-paying job, then you could purchase products that were there for you just the way you wanted, without the messiness of being in relationship with them. They would just perform like they should.

Even in relationship it seemed that people often aimed to not relate. They'd say, "I like your act, do you like mine too? You do your act with me, and I'll do my act with you. Okay? Is it a deal?" Let's get together and not actually meet, shall we?

Chapter Fifteen

At long last in came the big person Edward, who paused by the beige dryer to pick up Ponce. Looking at him more carefully now, Edward pondered perplexedly about who this was whom he had found at the back door. While examining Ponce, the big person Edward soon enough discovered that Ponce was not just a stuffed pig, but a puppet, and he put Ponce on his right hand. Ponce, despite all his recent trauma, had a chance to wave hello rather cheerily with his right forepaw and smile his best piggy smile, hoping that the big person would like him. The Edward person was a busy person, but he took a few moments to smile just a slight smile in return. And so it was that the big person Edward carried Ponce back into the house, two anonymous strangers having met face-to-face, rather intimately, just inside the backdoor, even though neither of them knew the other one's name.

The big person Edward decided to leave Ponce on the dining room table so that later in the day maybe at suppertime he would remember to ask his sweetheart Margot if she knew who Ponce was, and what he was doing here in their house. Had he rescued Ponce from abduction or had he received stolen booty from the neighborhood cat who snuck around going into other cats' houses and eating other cats' food while they were not looking. Maybe he'd done the same thing with Ponce, snuck in somewhere and snuck off with Ponce.

Even though Ponce did not know that he was "Ponce," he thought he knew who he was—a very precious creature indeed. Still he was in limbo, which meant bending over backwards to move forward in life. This was rather challenging for Ponce as he did not have much bend in him either forward or backward.

The big person Edward did not know whether he was a res-
cuer or an accomplice to thievery—it was a bit confusing—but
time would tell, and he'd deal with the consequences when
he knew what they were.

Now that they had bumped into each other—and there had
been a little bit of a spark of actually meeting—each of them
was wondering, who are you? And what are you doing here?
Is there something we mutually want to do together?

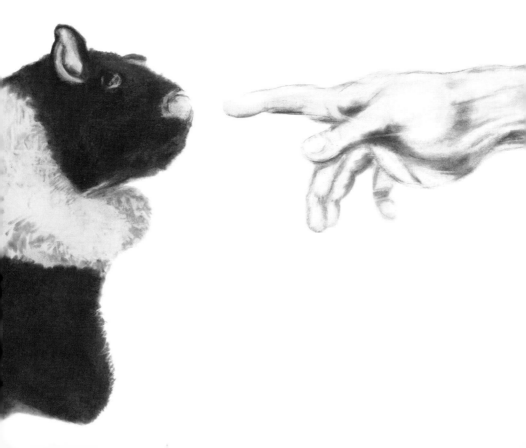

Chapter Sixteen

Sure enough, later in the day Edward's beloved sweetheart Margot came home. That was a happy occasion—and very reassuring—because even though Edward was in his sixties he still had abandonment issues, though not as severely as he once did. This meant that if you loved someone and someone loved you, like really truly, then you worried that they might leave and never come back again. They would say, "You insufferable person, I'm not living with you anymore." Or else one day they just wouldn't come home, and you'd be there by yourself, and your own self wasn't always a likeable person to spend time with. So if he, Edward, had such big problems living with himself, he could understand it that a beloved sweetheart might also find him tiresome and go away.

He would too, if only he could!

Chapter Seventeen

When Margot came home, Edward was busy preparing dinner, which was something he did because he rather liked cooking, and Margot liked his cooking too. She especially enjoyed his cooking when she was eating the food (more than the cooking when Edward was cooking because when Edward was cooking he would at times become intense and irritable, and you tried to stay out of his way). While eating, she would happily exalt, "This is so good! I am so lucky to have you cooking for me." This pleased Edward quite a bit because if she liked his cooking enough Edward supposed that she wouldn't leave, and that would be a good thing not to be abandoned, though of course he'd have to keep on cooking. Still Edward found that cooking for Margot was a great joy and pleasure, and Margot was prepared to wash dishes if it meant sitting down to beautiful food.

Maybe it meant that they loved one another! And that they belonged together in this world!

Chapter Eighteen

Most often when Margot came into the house from teaching school kids things they needed to know, like good grammar, and things they didn't need to know, like making art—finger-painting to music playing!—she would bring in the mail, as Edward mostly did not want to bother with getting bills and most every week yet another offer from AT&T. So it was that Margot passed through the kitchen, coming in the door that Ponce had been dragged out, and on into the dining room with its magnificent ever-so yellow walls, an ever-so yellow yellow stunning in its yellowness: sunshine, lemons, and daffodils (maybe sunflowers too!) all in the very same yellow, a yellow paint that Margot had picked out and procured—the very last can in the county before the new laws legislating less color in the world came into effect. As it is well known that color arouses emotions and emotions are not a good thing to have running around out in the world, we need to be united and make the world safe for drab!

On the other hand maybe if school kids learned how to play with colors they would enjoy greater well-being, and maybe grammar wasn't so important now that the whole world was sound bites and text messages.

Chapter Nineteen

When Margot went to put the mail down on the dining room table there was the stuffed pig, black and white like a police car, lying on its side. "What's my son's stuffed pig doing out here on the table?" she wanted to know. And Edward popped out from behind his pots and his cutting board, and said that's what he wanted to know too, only what he meant was that he didn't know that it was Pomme's piggy, and that now he knew that he had indeed caught Turtle the Cat in the act of attempting to haul off an adorable stuffed pig.

"What's his name?" asked Edward the chef come out of the kitchen, as he was once again picking up Ponce, and he and Ponce were once again innocently staring into each other's eyes. And Margot said that she couldn't remember.

A stuffed piggy without a name, a piggy hand-puppet that had almost been abducted and clearly needed a home; needed a home, a name, and lots of reassurances of belonging—this little piggy had weaseled its way into Edward's heart, and he decided to adopt.

Still the three of them had no clue that Ponce's name was Ponce. For now he was an almost anonymous orphan coming off the shelf and into someone's home and someone's heart.

Chapter Twenty

Over dinner Edward explained to Margot how he'd been in the side yard fussing about, and spied Turtle at the back door pouncing on his prey, and that he had not been sure if Turtle was on his way in or on his way out with what turned out to be a little stuffed piggy. Margot expressed her astonishment that Turtle had gone to the far end of the house, passing through the kitchen, through Edward's office, down the hallway, and into her office, leapt onto her chair, onto her desk, and then onto the top shelf of her bookcase in order to capture his prey. How daring that was! And Edward confessed that he had never really noticed Ponce on his high shelf in her office, so he had had no way of knowing that Ponce belonged here. And her son wasn't there to claim ownership either.

They agreed that they admired Turtle's audacity and clever individuality, and they wondered if Turtle kept his haul in some special place where people could go for their missing stuff if only they knew where Turtle kept his stash.

Now when they watched Turtle walk through their yard they could see that he was on the prowl—oh, was he good!— walking with a confident innocence, "Who me? What? How could you think that? I'm just out for a stroll." Prowling— that boy was a cat's cat: curious and top-dog-like for a cat, leader of the pack all on his own. But "Turtle?" More like "Captain Hook," "Pirate," or "Bluebeard." Of course being "Turtle" was way more inconspicuous, and permitted him to come out of his shell, raise the flag, launch a raid, and then go back undercover.

And he'd almost gotten away with it.

Chapter Twenty One

Stuffies had not always been a part of Edward's life. Oh, early on, there were stuffies, who all got together with him and his brother on Saturday mornings for a radio show called *No School Today* featuring "Big John and Sparky." That was after the orphanage where he and his brother had lived for four years, hardly ever seeing each other except for when little Eddie Bear was having a temper tantrum and needed a brother to see him through. Then the good ladies in charge of such things would let Dwite know that his little brother needed him. After Eddie Bear calmed down, his older brother was sent away.

It wouldn't be fair for the other kids who didn't have older brothers if his older brother could visit him, while they didn't have brothers who could. It wouldn't be fair.

Of course this was rather confusing—after all, how fair was it that their mommy had died? And their daddy had put them away? Eddie Bear was a few weeks past three, the youngest child in the whole wide orphanage—and also the smallest.

His eyeglasses to correct for his extreme far-sightedness made his eyes look huge when others looked at him. As he felt quite normal from inside, he did not realize that to others he was bug-eyed, and that, along with his pest-like smallness, might explain why he was occasionally swatted at.

Chapter Twenty Two

There'd been a teddy with Eddie Bear at the orphanage. Though he cannot recall the name of the bear, the orphanage was called Sunny Hills. When "Sunny Hills" was spoken, it was said rather quickly and a bit apologetically with more emphasis on Hills, "sunny HILLS," and it never sounded actually sunny, where you could spread out and relax like at the beach or in a meadow. The "ny" or "knee" was short and swallowed, rather than spacious and welcoming, almost not there: "suhny H-i-l-l-s. Nobody said it like, "oh, what a beautiful sunne-e day, where you might want to linger expansively on the "knee." And truth be told the Hills themselves were a bit dark. It's not like there were woods or anything. After all this was sunny California—darkness masquerading as beautiful surfaces—with its dry grassy hills dotted with oaks, but especially at night things could sneak up on you.

And sometimes little Eddie Bear wished he could scream, "Get out of my bed," but maybe it was all a dream, and it was hard to scream when you were asleep.

Chapter Twenty Three

After dinner that first night when Edward had decided to adopt, he took Ponce, this newly discovered precious creature, away from the dining room in one door of the kitchen and out another door leading to a half flight of stairs that went up to the master bedroom. Ponce could not remember when, if ever, he had been held so tenderly, and here was yet another part of the house where he had never been, and it was pretty exciting to be seeing new sights after a couple of years on the shelf and before that shut away in boxes. In some ways it wasn't much of a master bedroom seeing as there was no adjoining bathroom, but there were windows on two sides of the room and enough distinctive (rather than merely nice and pleasant) art on the walls to make it feel like someone lived there. Ponce surprised himself with his art sensibility, guessing that he had been picking up on some of Margot's esthetic while he was on the shelf in her office.

Inside the bedroom Edward turned left, and Ponce's heart leapt, as there at the head of the bed was a whole family of stuffies, a rather unlikely family to be sure as there were various sorts of critters who seemed to be getting along just fine. Before he could stop himself, Ponce was squealing in delight seeing his old friend Hobbes, a tiger (also from Pomme's childhood), "Hobbes, I never thought I'd see you again."

The room was a-dazzle—Ponce picked up on the conviviality, and was smitten. Soon enough, Ponce, the little black and white piggy, was bouncing on the bed with the others, and Edward was introducing or re-introducing them one by one: the tiger of course was, "Hobbes," who rather styled himself after the Hobbes of literary fame; a cinnamon brown bear with European airs was known as "Zimt;" a roundish koala bear—obviously an Aussie—and thus called, "Ozzie," or "Oz" for short; and a soft white rabbit with the unlikely name of "Euphorbia." Pretty quickly it was hard to keep track.

Still other critters sat and reclined on the shelf at the head of the bed: Wilbur, a hand-puppet dog; Savoy, a gay rabbit; and Swami Binkiananda, a small fit-in-your-hand bunny who could squeak when people squeezed him between their fingers. Squeaks, squeals, whines, groans, pontifications: his wide-ranging vocabulary had brought him fame as a Swami, and his irreverence had earned the name Binky. Deep issues could be addressed to the Swami simply by asking, "Hey Bink, what do you think?"

Meeting all the others, Ponce began sensing that he was not being judged or blamed, and that he could be who he was without being put down or looked down on, scorned or distanced, as though he didn't really fit in or belong. He wasn't being lightly assessed by know-it-alls who knew all about who was who, what was what, who was IN and who was OUT.

How rare was that. He could be himself. And shine.

Chapter Twenty Four

Edward was explaining to the other critters that this little piggy had come to move in with them—that he was an orphan like all of them—and would they please be friendly and welcoming, and do everything they could to make the little piggy feel at home—to include him in their conversations and invite him into their games even though he wouldn't know all the rules and all the small talk needed to keep up.

Edward also assured the other stuffies that the little piggy's heart was in the right place, and soon enough they would hear all about his adventures in the world, and that Edward and the small stuffie didn't know what his name was, and could they please get to know the true pig really well, well enough to name him his true name, just like each of them had found their true names, the names that resonated deeply inside their stuffiness.

Then Edward left the room, leaving the family of stuffies having grown one larger. The little piggie without even thinking about it began humming inside, in fact he began to hum all over. That was a wonderful feeling that Ponce had never felt before. At first he didn't know what to make of it. Then little by little, the suspicion began to dawn, and then came the sun rise of knowing —even though it was nighttime—that the hum was...well... the hum was...he himself.

And he was happy.

Chapter Twenty Five

Later in the evening Edward came to bed. As was his custom
he brought a glass of water with him to put by the bedside,
which was maybe not such a good idea. Probably he wasn't
drinking enough water during the day—so many people had
been telling him to drink more water including his psychic
("I see you need to drink more water.") —because he would
get thirsty at night, drink water, and then need to pee. That
meant a lot of getting in and out of bed, but every time he
got back into bed he would be sure to find the little black and
white piggy and make sure that the piggy felt close and cozy
with him, reassuring him that he belonged in this bed, in this
world, at this time.

Edward was feeling that if he did this with the piggy, maybe
the piggy would be doing this with him.

Also if Edward was doing this with the piggy, perhaps he was
really doing this with himself: "You belong here, little Eddie,"
he could be saying, even though that was not the piggy's
name and the piggy was way too small to be big enough to be
little Eddie.

Chapter Twenty Six

Soon the day came when the little piggy found out his name was Ponce. It was a Sunday morning shortly after he had joined the household—rather than being a shelf ornament. Many people relax on Sunday mornings, sleep in, read the Sunday funnies, drink too much coffee, and wait for pro football to come on the telly. But for Edward it was often a work day, and that was the case on this particular Sunday, when he was scheduled to put on his formal robes and give a Zen talk at Green Gulch Farm. What would he say?

This question was complicated by the fact that this particular Sunday lecture—it being the first one of the month—was supposed to begin with a ten or fifteen minute talk "for the kids," and many, if not most of the kids would be sitting in the laps of their mommies or daddies. How does one talk to people who are this small? What does one say that will speak to them? It had been a rather long time since Edward had been this small, and he was a bit out of practice with how to have this kind of conversation. Not only was he many years removed from that age group, but so was his daughter. As he would say during this part of his talk, "My little girl is thirty-eight now." And he might have added, "Heaven help me"—not that his daughter hadn't grown up into a fine beautiful woman, but that so many years had passed while she was doing that.

Edward by profession was not a kindergarten teacher or a pre-school teacher, but here he was, being directed to "teach them (these little people) something about Buddhism."

Chapter Twenty Seven

Edward would often look around for things to talk about: inside and out and about. Inside there were thoughts and feelings and sensations, and if he was particularly quiet, open, and receptive, and if he looked a little cross-eyed, which he did quite naturally, things to talk about would appear, and nobody could say where these things came from.

Other times he would be looking around the room for something to say, as though things to say were just sitting around waiting to be noticed the way the little pig on the shelf had been noticed—by the cat of all people! Of course it wasn't quite that simple. Rather that his eyes would find something to settle on, and this object would spark his imagination or inspiration. And even that didn't really describe the process. It wasn't that he was looking around for anything in particular, but that things *popped* into view. And when they *popped* into view, they often had something to say. And so it was on that Sunday morning that the little black and white piggy *popped* into view and had something to say.

The piggy who was just about to become Ponce could hardly contain himself as he spilled out his lifelong dream to entertain kids who were small enough to sit in their mommy's or daddy's lap.

Chapter Twenty Eight

"Help me out here, Mr. Edward," the piggy enthused, "help me realize my passion to be a performer." "Mr. Edward indeed," Edward startled, "though I appreciate the respect that you are showing me, you needn't address me as Mister as between you and me, we are both fairly small, and Mister is too large and grown-up a word to be applied to me, though my humble personage seems to be in the auspicious position of helping your dreams come true."

(Meanwhile Edward had been realizing that the little piggy had grown up with Margot's son Pomme who had been acting for much of his young life, and then gone off to the University of Michigan to pursue his dreams—leaving Ponce behind along with several other stuffies. Living with an aspiring actor as the little piggy had for many years, it would not be surprising if this same little piggy had big dreams of his own.) Having clarified that they were not to be on formal terms with one another, Edward placed the piggy puppet on his right hand and confided that if they were to collaborate on a performance, then the piggy would need to have a name. What would it be?

Over the previous days Edward had tried out a number of names: Arnold, Claude, Fred, Licorice, but none of them had stuck, and many of them he could no longer remember. And so he was despairing a bit as he explained the situation to the critter with the small black eyes, crinkly ears, and happy snout.

"You need a name," said Edward, "that I can remember! How about one that ends with 'the Pig?'"

Chapter Twenty Nine

And there it was—like the ringing of a bell in empty space—
"Ponce! Ponce the Pig."

Even though Ponce had a beautiful happy snout, he did not
really have much of a mouth, nonetheless his lips were moving with Edward's. That was an exciting moment as both of
them realized the name was exactly right, and Ponce began to
clap his paws together, and if he could have done cartwheels
he certainly would have. Instead, to continue celebrating this
moment of insight Ponce found himself jumping up and
down on Edward's hand.

Once Ponce had calmed down a bit, Edward explained that
there was once someone named, "Ponce de Leon," who went
searching for the Fountain of Youth in Florida (and that
people continue this search to this day in Florida). And that
growing up, he (Edward) had always said the Ponce in Ponce
de Leon with one syllable, "Ponce" like "bounce" or "ounce"
only without the "ow!" sound, but more of an "on" sound
like in pond—"Ponce." But Ponce the Pig was to be "POHN-
say," perhaps as it might be pronounced in French if Edward
could find the accent agui on his typewriter.

Once the two of them had completed this informal naming
ceremony, Edward turned to Ponce and said, "All right, then,
Ponce the Pig, if it would delight you, it would delight me
if you would come with me to help give the "Kids Talk" at
Green Gulch. I am guessing that you could be something of
a star and attract a lot of attention, and take that attention
off of me."

Then Edward clarified with Ponce not to worry if people laughed.

The audience wouldn't be laughing at them. They would be enjoying themselves, and releasing some of the tension that goes with aiming to get it right all of the time. And that releasing tension was probably a good thing, though you could never tell for sure.

If you weren't stressing you might be enjoying your time here on planet earth, and who knows what you would do in that case.

(Whoops! Not knowing what you might do could be stressful. And though this is quite a funny situation, few people are laughing.)

Chapter Thirty

So Edward packed up his robe bag—which was an old green canvas LL Bean zippered bag with leather straps. Once it had been bright and outgoing the way those giant squash leaves blossomed expansively, but now it was dull and headed towards colorless, and what had once been a useful shoulder strap was nowhere to be seen. Time was responsible for these changes, but time was elusive and not at all ready to be held accountable for the mischief it was making. Still if you were young, you counted on time to help you grow up, and if you were heart-broken you wanted time to heal the wound. It wasn't at all clear whether or not time knew what it was doing. Maybe it was a child of the sixties –"I'm just doing my thing." And then that annoying post script, "Deal with it."

Packing up the robe bag meant that Edward had to be sure that he had all of the requisite items that would turn him into a masterful Zen person: the white jiban, the beige kimono, the dark brown obi, the black koromo, a thick black cord that was used as a robe belt. On top of this would go his coffee-latte-colored okesa. Also there was a handsome stick, carved from rose wood to resemble a back scratcher, that his teacher Sojun had given him. Known as *the mind that reaches everywhere*, when you held it you were the boss, even though you were nothing but a mosquito trying to bite an iron bull.

Check, check, check, if you were going to be a Zen person, it was important to be masterful, and nothing said masterful like fine robes. Unfortunately Edward's were getting to be threadbare, especially if you looked closely, so everyone knew that he was over-the-hill just like his robes, a teacher that some conceded, "might be good for beginners." Ponce on the other hand looked quite fresh, even dazzling (if this could be said of a stuffed piggy) and full of himself with his pristine black and white fuzzy stuff which was a perfect match for the mostly black, a little white, colors of Zen.

Somebody, when the time came and the curtain rose, was ready to seize the day.

Chapter Thirty One

Edward's sweetheart Margot decided to come with them for the trip to Green Gulch Farm where Edward, the announced speaker, and Ponce, the unannounced non-speaker, were to perform. Margot didn't always come with Edward Bear on his speaking engagements, but being a big fan of the theater she was eager to see Edward and Ponce performing together.

Edward and Margot had met thirty years ago at the Zen Center back in the day when Zen Center was still an empire with great real estate holdings and several businesses: a restaurant called Greens, a grocery store named the Green Gulch Green-grocer, a Tassajara Bread Bakery, a bookstore, a print shop, a cushion and clothes shop, along with an Abbot, who had met the Rolling Stones through his friend who was in the record business. Also the Abbot was traveling periodically to the Soviet Union on personal peace missions. So clearly, the Abbot was an important person, and he needed two full-time assistants plus a household attendant and an incense-carrier at each of the three Zen Center locations, where he had three houses and three libraries. In awe young Edward would listen while the Abbot proclaimed that Zen meant giving up your ego, and the best way to give up your ego was doing what he told you to do.

You might not be meeting the Rolling Stones, but the Abbot who told you what to do would be meeting them, so you knew you were contributing to an important cause, and sometimes when he was telling you what to do, you could be in the same room with him—rather than on the phone. As long as you didn't stop to think about it *too* much, that was pretty thrilling.

Plus his robes were magnificent, quite an assortment of them! Wasn't he so dashing and intrepid when he was dressed for the occasion in one of his splendid outfits?

Chapter Thirty Two

So it was back in the empire days that Margot and Edward had one date the evening that they ran into each other in the Page Street crosswalk outside the red brick City Center building. Unbeknownst to Edward, this Margot person had her eye on him, seeing him as especially special, and so in the crosswalk (which was way, way less busy thirty years ago) she said, "Hello," and, "how are you?" and Edward had replied, "Fine, and how are you?" "Quite all right," Margot had responded, "it's my birthday!"

Probably by now they had found their way to the curb, and Edward aiming to be friendly, and not just supremely enlightened and masterful, exclaimed, "Well, happy birthday! –and do you have some plans for how to celebrate?" When Margot confessed that she didn't have any plans, Edward invited her to dinner, and she was gracious enough to accept.

They headed for the Santa Fe Bar and Grill which was on University Avenue in Berkeley in what was rumored to be the old train station. Mark Miller was the chef, and he had created an exciting Southwest menu utilizing lots of different chilies and salsas. Yum. When they got back to San Francisco and were back in the crosswalk, Edward kissed her goodnight, and they went their separate ways.

Thirty years later they went on a second date. Edward had given one of his Green Gulch lectures and ran into Margot in the residents' hall there in front of the little altar that had a beautiful Kwan Yin statue to greet you. This time after their hellos and how are yous, Margot asked him (rather shyly) if he would be interested in going on a "play date." A *play date* was not something that Edward knew anything about, so he confessed that he was not sure what that was: "Is it a date where we play together? or will we be playing at dating?" Margot answered that either one would be fine with her, and Edward, still somewhat mystified by the concept, said, "Well... okay." And they made a plan to make a plan.

Now they were driving to Green Gulch together with Ponce and a bag of well-worn robes.

Chapter Thirty Three

Ponce was very excited on the trip to Green Gulch, sitting in the front seat propped between Edward's legs, where he could almost reach the steering wheel. Of course he could not see the road, but even being nose-level with the bottom of the steering wheel was an improvement over traveling in the dark in a box.

When they arrived at Green Gulch, Ponce was whisked off with Edward and his robes to a small upstairs room that the Tanto (Head of Practice) let Edward use to change clothes. Ponce sat on small black hip-high table while Edward began getting out of his street clothes and into Buddha's clothes. Edward was surprisingly happy, even happy-go-lucky, which was a surprise because often enough before one of his lectures he was nowhere near happy and certainly not happy-go-lucky. More like mortified.

Edward would have to give a talk to a high level group of people who liked to think they knew their stuff and were quite discriminating about who they would listen to. And they would sit there very silently assessing how wise the words were that they were hearing. And poor Edward would worry that his words would not be nearly enlightening enough to please the assembly.

Even though everyone was generally polite and well-behaved, there might come the time when they would rise up and want to tear him apart. It could happen, you know. It might be his day to die!

Chapter Thirty Four

In fact speaking in front of the assembly was considered to be one of the five most fearful things in life, right up there with agonizing over losing you life, your body, your mind, or your livelihood. Sensing that you might not survive was indeed scary, so often you needed to sit down and make use of the toilette before leaving home. As long as he was giving Dharma Talks, Edward did not have to worry about being constipated, that was for sure.

But he still had to worry about what to say. Years and years ago when he was a fresh-faced, shaved-headed Zen student listening to talk after talk by various teachers which often went over his head or referred to fuzzy things floating in his head, Edward had decided that if he was ever the one giving the talk, he would aim to speak directly to his audience: heart to heart, body to body, presence to presence. Not just head to head, as though that was the way to educate the listeners about what was what.

There was something vacant about that—nobody seemed to be home, and the TV was going anyway: what show was it? Where was the speaker? Where was the listener? Perhaps it would be vaguely embarrassing if someone spoke to someone, and they actually met one another.

"Ponce," he explained, "we're here to be seen! To touch people's hearts. To connect directly." Ponce was curious, yet unconcerned, as he did not have any intellectual material to share in any case. He didn't have much choice about it—he would be himself, a sincere stuffed piggy, and perhaps some would see him for who he was *inside:* a magnificent spiritual *being.* So it was that Ponce shared Edward's belief that revealing yourself was a way to *deeply honor* your audience and warm their hearts. Even though some in the audience were sure to be dismissive—how childish is that, bringing a stuffed piggy into an important dharma talk?

Still those who could have their hearts tickled and touched might relax, realizing that who they really were was not their *appearance* or their *performance.* Maybe they would learn the secret that Kabir the mystic poet mentioned was most intimate: the *breath inside the breath.* Presence.

Chapter Thirty Five

Once Edward was dressed for the occasion with his white jiban, beige kimono, black koromo, black robe belt, and coffee-latte okesa, he picked up the alert and bright-eyed Ponce and told him what he had in mind. "Ponce, my dear, I'm going to put you in the left sleeve of my kimono, and when the time comes after I've done the rituals, I'll pull you out. Are you good with that?" Ponce nodded, and then they rehearsed, so that Edward was sure that he could reach his right hand into his left sleeve and into the opening that Ponce provided for a hand. Once Ponce was on Edward's hand, he was to pop dramatically into view and leap to life.

Out the door and down the stairs they went. A few steps across the wooden floor of the residents' hall in front of the Kwan Yin Altar, they met Edward's disciple Valorie, who was also known as *Patient Mountain Harmonious Spirit.* She and Edward bowed to each other, and Ponce ventured out of Edward's sleeve to say hello. First off he put his little paws together and bowed, and Valorie reciprocated with a bow of her own. Right away Valorie struck him with how receptive she was to his presence, as he had certainly experienced many people being quite dismissive of mere stuffed animals. "Ponce," she exclaimed, "How are you?" and it was as though she meant every word(!): *How...are...you?* Meant the words, meant him, was actually concerned about his well-being. So it was that Ponce was smitten with Valorie's patient harmonious spirit. Where were these people when he was stuffed away in boxes?

"Ready for your debut, precious?" Ponce nodded. And Valorie concluded, "Whatever happens, you'll be fine. See you inside." *Inside,* thought Ponce, that was clever. She'll see me inside. Where everything is connected.

Chapter Thirty Six

Cozy back in Edward's sleeve, Ponce began hearing a big bell resounding as they headed for the zendo, and realized that the air was vibrant with anticipation. Entering the zendo, all the energy in the room seemed to be accumulating in Ponce's head (especially since he was upside down inside the sleeve), making him dizzy. Edward was bowing, and Ponce was getting bounced around. This acting business challenged one's wherewithal in ways you never expected. What was next? With no lines to forget, Ponce decided to relax in his spaciness.

Then Edward was sitting and straightening his robes. A small bell, "clunked," and the room was awash with chanting: *"An unsurpassed, penetrating, and perfect Dharma is rarely met with even in a hundred thousand million kalpas...."* Ponce could hear Edward saying good morning to all the kids and their mommies and daddies, hoping that they'd had a wonderful summer full of fun activities. Then Edward was mentioning that he'd brought along a small friend to help with his talk, and that he would see if his friend would come out even though he could be a bit shy at times.

"Shy," raged Ponce to himself, "how about dazed with upside-down-shook-around?" Still it was showtime, and he endeavored to put on his most charming expression as he was emerging from Edward's sleeve. Suddenly from out of the dark, Ponce was in a huge hall with rows and rows of people sitting in chairs, while right in front of him were small children sitting with their mommies and daddies—and everybody was staring at him. Promptly he forgot all the lines he didn't have, painfully conscious of his lack of training.

In spite of all his excitement and eagerness about appearing on stage, when the headlights flashed out of the dark, he was the deer, frozen in space. Fight or flight was out of the question. Ponce waved timidly. The show must go on.

Chapter Thirty Seven

Then Edward was describing how Ponce had almost been abducted by the neighbor's cat Turtle, and how scary it was, asking the kids for their empathy and understanding. Wouldn't it be terrible if you were taken from your house by a stranger? Ponce had the feeling that the kids were yawning, but what did he know? Apparently many people have difficulties relating to stuffed piggies at Zen talks. While some of the kids were smiling, others were looking to their mommies and daddies asking wordlessly, "What am I to do with *this?*"

Once Edward had endeavored to introduce Ponce and engage the children's awareness, he then wanted to teach the kids about the four vows—especially he wanted to teach them a version of singing the four vows that he had heard when he visited Toledo, Ohio.

Normally the four vows—very important vows they are—are chanted with the best deep mellifluous monotone that one can muster:
Sentient beings are numberless, I vow to save them.
Desires are inexhaustible, I vow to put an end to them.
Dharma gates are boundless, I vow to enter them.
Buddha's Way is unsurpassable, I vow to attain it.

You are committing yourself to something impossible, which is rather like life itself: you were planning to do what? (The standard line being that if you want to make God laugh, tell him your plans.) The sentiments were perfectly laudable, explained Edward, and well worth voicing, as you aim to express your innermost wishes for yourself and others.

No problem with that.

Chapter Thirty Eight

Edward then went on to explain to the kids, while Ponce
listened in as well, that he wanted to teach them another
version where you sing, which he said he had heard the kids
singing, and singing quite energetically, in Toledo, Ohio and
by golly, if the kids could sing the four vows in Toledo, Ohio
we could do that here in California as well. Please join in.
And he commenced singing:

We're going to wake up all the beings in the world...all the beings...
We're going to put endless heartache to rest... achey breakey heart...
We're going to walk through every wisdom gate...
walkin' on through...
We're going to live the great Buddha's Way... yes we will!...

The audience especially loved the little add-ons at the end of
the lines—that was a start. The tune was more or less blue-
grass/country-western, and Ponce found himself bouncing
along with the music. This wasn't as easy as you might think,
because Edward could not keep a tune for the life of him,
and Ponce was a bit embarrassed to be dancing to an out-of-
tune singer. Oh well.

They plunged ahead—Edward asking the kids (and everyone)
to join in singing the four vows, and he told them that they
didn't have to worry about not keeping the tune since he
couldn't do that either. Do some drumming...shout out the
end of the lines, he suggested, and began singing again.

Though he really was not very good at all of this, Edward
persisted in singing anyway, putting his whole heart into
it—and soon enough Ponce was delightedly waving his fore-

paws and swaying to and fro with the best of them, in fact he probably was the best of them, as the room clearly had mixed feelings about whether or not to join in—after all, what was happening to their old-time true religion? As Edward's friend Rinsen had said in Toledo, when Edward mentioned that he loved the singing version even though it was not traditional: "When I first heard it, I must admit, my cheeks *tightened*."

Finally Edward was congratulating the audience for their participation and thanking them for their presence and their attention, and wishing them well, especially the kids and their parents who would be leaving to go to the kids' program, while the lecture continued...for adults only...unless some kids insisted on staying. Slowly the front portion of the audience began making its way towards the exits, which gave Edward a chance to say hello and Ponce a chance to wave cheerily to the little boys and girls who braved passing by, really closely to them, on their way out.

Though questions were in the air: Where *am* I? What am I doing *here*? And you could see that they felt rather shy and timid, the boys and girls were sincerely sincere, and one or two of them even stopped to shake the fore-paw that Ponce extended to them. "Hello! And good day to you too!" said Ponce.

Chapter Thirty Nine

Who knows what people need to hear, or what will shift their lives in new and especially auspicious directions? Ponce was wondering about this, and getting ready to settle himself at Edward's feet, to sit quietly and expectantly, waiting to see if this would happen to him, an auspicious revelation of some sort, when Valorie appeared from off to the side. "Edward," she asked, "would you like me to take Ponce and hold him while you proceed with your Dharma Talk?"

Edward agreed to this, and Ponce would have squealed with excitement if only he had a squealer to activate. His new best-friend Valorie was offering to hold him, and probably it would be really close to her heart. Ponce was over-the-top delighted.

Shortly Ponce was snuggling in Valorie's arms, tenderly caressed, and he began to feel tingly and warm all over, through and through. Maybe this was the "transmission outside the scriptures" that Ponce had heard Zen offered! (of course the Pope had cautioned people to watch out for that warm and tingly fuzzy stuff that might lead them astray.) It had been such a long time, if ever, that Ponce had been enveloped with this much love, and nestling down, he soon realized that he was terribly exhausted from all the morning's exertions.

Soon enough, almost immediately, he was fast asleep, and missed all of Edward's talk, only waking up when Valorie uncrossed her legs, and began to stand. Ponce felt truly blissed-out. Maybe words weren't so important after all, when you could be snuggling in the lap of *Patient Mountain Harmonious Spirit.*

It was like Big Mind—always on your side.

Chapter Forty

Back home Ponce was little by little becoming acquainted with his new companions. His old friend Hobbes with his handsome stripes was clearly the ring-leader, a magnificent creature who sprawled luxuriously and floppily on the bed. This rather good-natured tiger—Margot kept a Sharpie smile in place on his face—had had his whiskers singed previously so that they were crinkly and only on one side of his face. Still he managed to venture through most of his life with a wry, mischievous, up-beat air—when he wasn't snoozing. Ponce didn't know much, but he was reminded pretty fast that this critter was obviously an instigator who rarely took no for an answer. You were prey or an accessory to preying—unless he was tired, and then you'd better let him sleep.

His latest prank was to engage in affection attacks where he would leap on the chest and face of the larger critters while they were happily reading—shouting, "Affection attack, affection attack," and then be sure to kiss their eyes and nose and whatever else he could get to before they got their defenses up. Sometimes the big people had to tell him rather forcefully, "Cool it, Hobbes, time for bed," and then he'd droop and withdraw pouting, only to return shortly into close proximity where he was insanely good at snuggling his floppiness over and around the larger critters.

Years ago Margot had spent many hours seeking out Hobbes to join her household when her son Pomme was a fan of the comic in which Hobbes appeared with a smart aleck boy named Calvin. So Hobbes became a veteran of domestic households with a growing boy, who aspired to be an actor. Left behind when Pomme departed for Ann Arbor and the University, Hobbes had spotted his chance for a new life when Margot moved in with Edward. *Fresh meat*, thought Hobbes, and it was a good thing he didn't share that thought with Edward until much later, as Edward had once attended a pilates class, where the teacher called him, *Fresh meat,* for an hour and a half. Once he got out of that class, he didn't go back. *Fresh meat* was just *not* in keeping with his idea of himself.

At the same time Edward found that Hobbes was just his *cup of tea*, not that Edward ever mentioned that to Hobbes either. (*Cup of tea*, indeed! Harumph!) Instead, Edward would say things like, "You're my boy, Hobbes," and he'd let Hobbes tickle his nose with those crinkly whiskers.

Chapter Forty One

Another mainstay in Ponce's new tribe was the cinnamon bear named Zimt, who wore what had once been a dashing red ribbon around his neck. While some bears were certainly better dressed than Zimt with entire outfits from boutique outlets, their bodies were rather on the stiff side, and Zimt reveled in his flexibility, maintaining a debonair quality in keeping with his continental name "Zimt," which was German for cinnamon. He was *not* just "Cinnamon Bear," but "Zimt," a German bear who was cultured and civilized.

Where he came from people could actually travel on public transportation without waiting for exhausting periods of time. You did not need to have your own car to go everywhere in way too much traffic and stress about finding a parking place. You walked a block or two and hopped on a bus or the metro. There were even schedules posted and in many places signs that hung from the ceiling of the subway with the yellow lettering that told you, "3 minutes" or "5 minutes" for which subway train—and where they were going. Once aboard then you could read or listen to your iPod without worrying about cars stopping suddenly, or lights changing green to yellow to red just in time to stop your progress.

How relaxing was that?

Chapter Forty Two

Zimt explained to Ponce that Edward had found him marooned in an ice cream and candy shop at The Barnyard, a shopping center at the mouth of Carmel Valley. The Barnyard, an excellent example of California living, had shops on different levels with pleasant walkways, flower beds, trees, and shrubs, here and there some graciously designed steps. All year long the flowers were blooming—they never stopped! And the sun was always shining, or at least it felt that way, even though the fog rolled in many days of the year.

You could buy clothes and kitchen stuff, jewelry, and of course, being just down the street from Carmel, a very exclusive place priding itself on having had Clint Eastwood as its mayor for a time, you could certainly find art galleries. And maybe if you became tired from flinging your money around, you would want to have something to eat—all kinds of options were available.

For years and years the centerpiece of this California Shopping Experience was a large beautiful bookstore called the Thunderbird. Not only handsomely arranged book shelves and tables for browsing, but an adjacent café, other smaller rooms for art and music—a Destination Bookstore. But no more—how unsettling to walk up the gentle slopes and find a boarded-up business. Those of us who had grown up with the business since the mid-60s going back to its original location, had known the owners, had found a home away from home, we mourned.

Conviviality? It's too expensive to bring people together.

Unless you have a gigantic chain of coffee shops, where people are fueling up to get back on the move.

Chapter Forty Three

At the time that Edward met Zimt he had not had a teddy bear since he was a small boy of eight or nine years old, and that adorable bear's name has been long forgotten. And gosh, that bear had suffered terribly towards the end of his time here. And poor Edward, having been the cause of this torment, had not had a bear ever since, as he had become a grown-up person and left stuffed animals behind him. Also of course he wasn't sure that he could trust himself with another bear after his first bear had been treated so unspeakably.

The original bear had been a soft, but sturdy, richly colored brown bear with a yellowy forehead and yellow at the end of his feet and paws. And he had been about three times the size of Zimt—or else Edward himself had been a lot smaller. The old bear had been about half of Edward's size, at least originally, only Edward had kept growing. Old photos show a small boy clutching his teddy—quite happily enamored with this beautiful creature.

Then quite unexpectedly things changed. Sometime after Edward's four years at the orphanage, Sunny Hills, where things were dark and unexplained, where he had wanted to say, "get your hands off of me," sometime after he had moved in with his brother, his father, and his father's new wife, this little boy found that his bear was misbehaving.

His bear tried and tried to do things just right, just the way that little Eddie wanted them done, and still it was not good enough for the troubled boy. And every time the bear misbe-haved, little Eddie put the bear's nose right in his butt. For his teddy bear the smell was horrible. For his good-hearted brown bear it was completely demeaning and de-humanizing, and try as the little bear would try, he could not behave well enough to avoid this humiliation.

Little Eddie kept believing that if his bear were punished in this way then the little bear would certainly learn his lesson, but somehow this never seemed to happen, and little Eddie kept finding something that the bear did wrong, something that needed punishment. His poor sweet bear kept trying and trying to behave well enough, until finally the life went out of him.

To this day it is Edward's most painful shameful memory, to have tormented a blessedly sweet good-hearted stuffed animal out of his own confusion and misunderstanding: re-enacting in a sadly twisted way his own humiliation. Bless his heart: the little bear's and little Eddie's.

Chapter Forty Four

At the time it had all seemed so reasonable, *so* reasonable and *so* important, to put that little bear's nose right next to a smelly butt. Certainly that would fix everything, wouldn't it? Yet nothing was made whole, nothing was restored to grace, a beautiful creature suffered torment, and no one felt any better at all. What a shame.

Then the little boy who had become a grown man or at least someone who looked like a grown man—the man who as a little boy had tormented a little bear—met Zimt in a candy shop. And without even thinking about it, his heart went out to the cinnamon bear with the red ribbon around his neck, and he thought, well, maybe, he could buy himself a new bear to really care for this time. So he consulted his Vipassana teacher who was with him at the time, "Do you suppose it would be okay for a grown man to buy himself a sweet little bear as his very own?"

"If you welcome him into your heart, you will never regret it." It was as if the heavens opened.

Chapter Forty Five

So Zimt explained to Ponce that he had known Edward for goodness gracious, it must be twenty years, and most nights they had snuggled together even and especially when Edward went off to Europe and Maine and Toronto, Austin, Boston, Sacramento, and Gualala.

Edward had to travel a lot to earn enough money to pay the mortgage and the property taxes, so that he would have a home where he didn't live. And then he could tell people where it was that he didn't live. Some people found this deeply Zen, while most people "tsked, tsked" at the nature of our modern world where people not living where they lived was taken for granted.

At home or away, Edward was most kind and concerned with his cinnamon bear's well-being, as most days, for instance, sitting him up in bed during the day rather than leaving him lying face down as though he was a hung-over drunk. So fear not, Zimt assured Ponce, Edward could not be more kind and solicitous.

And so it was. Well...most of the time.

Chapter Forty Six

It wasn't long after the lecture at Green Gulch, where Ponce helped give the kids' lecture teaching the kids to sing the four vows, that Edward asked Ponce if he would like to come with him on a road trip to San Luis Obispo, Morro Bay, and Los Osos. Zimt, he explained, had grown tired of traveling, so Hobbes had been coming along with him, and now he and Hobbes wanted to welcome Ponce by inviting him to come along on their next trip.

Ponce was overjoyed: a new adventure, seeing the world, getting out of town. Not only was he out of the box and off of the shelf, he would be going places, and he wasn't being asked to forsake his integrity to do so. He was a dear, sincere, whole-hearted, lovable, little stuffed piggy, and that was that—understood!

Edward agreed with Ponce, that he would do his best to see Ponce's true heart and true virtue—of course, he would do his best.

Little did anyone know what lay in store for them down the road.

Chapter Forty Seven

Somehow it ended up being a very busy few days for Edward getting ready for his trip, even though he had cancelled his ear-cleaning appointment—that was just too much. There was so much to do before leaving, very important things that were not so very important: harvesting the apples and pears, juicing them and dehydrating them; folding up the plastic bags that had been air-drying on the bottles on the floor so that they could easily fit in a neat stack inside a zip-lock plastic bag that could easily go to the grocery store to be reused; taking out the trash including the bottles and cans, paper, and yard waste which now included kitchen scraps, which in Edward's case went out to a corner of the yard where you dug a hole and buried them. There was also trash-trash, a rather small bag each week if you were not buying gobs of packaging along with your food.

Before leaving home Edward always felt an obligation to straighten up, just in case he didn't come back—you wouldn't want to leave a mess for others to clean up for you. Also he wanted his home to be somewhat in order in case he returned. It could happen you know. In fact it always had, at least so far.

The other important thing was to be caring for or participating in his on-going relationships with family, friends, students, and acquaintances, so his last evening before the trip he spent visiting with a young American woman from San Francisco who had been ordained as a Zen priest and was living at a temple in Japan. They cooked dinner together, and Moon Heart, shorn of hair, told him how much she loved Japanese culture and her Japanese Zen teacher. It was not a problem to spend the evening visiting. Edward would just get up at four-thirty in the morning to pack.

Isn't it always that simple?

Chapter Forty Eight

Six hours sleep might be enough when you are a young person–one young friend of Edward's had proudly proclaimed having gotten "eleven hours sleep," pause, "in the last four days." That was about four days before he came down with pneumonia. So maybe it's a good idea not to sleep so little, even when you are young.

Sure enough, next day, four-thirty in the morning, up popped Edward from his sleepiness. Heading downstairs to shower, he knew to take Ponce and Hobbes with him to the dining room table—no wasted movements, no extra trip up the stairs later to get those lazy critters out of bed. Hobbes sprawled out on the table, promptly snoozing, while Ponce sat alertly watching everything that was happening. He was being honored with his first road trip outside of the box that he had always traveled in previously, so he didn't want to miss anything.

First Edward went and showered, trusting that would help wake him up, along with the coffee that followed. That's when Ponce saw him next, coming back to the rose-wood table with his mug of coffee and his official Packing List. Already he had checked off the two most important items on his list, Ponce and Hobbes. Then he started down the rest of the list: t-shirts, underwear, one pair of shorts, an extra pair of long pants, short-sleeved white collar polo shirts with pockets to wear under his black Zen hippari, and his rakusu, a small Buddhist robe which had his Japanese name on the back in case he'd forgotten or needed Zen ID.

Then the list got more complicated: stove-top espresso maker, coffee, thermos, teas, Chinese herbal extracts, a small cup for tea, a larger cup (with a lid!) for coffee, stuff for lunch on the road: sliced apples and peanut butter, sliced cheese, radishes lightly salted, organic dark chocolate. Ponce began noticing that dear Edward was starting to stress. This jump-started Ponce's worry that maybe he should be doing something to help, only to decide that sitting quietly and mindfully probably was helpful in its way. After all he wasn't going to start running around the house snatching up things for Edward to take: he wouldn't know what to get, his front paws were near to useless for picking things up, and he lacked the rear legs for ambulating effectively.

Edward had begun making a new list handwritten down the right hand side of the printed list, all the things that he had not yet gotten: toiletries, computer, and a whole pile—good Gosh—of stuff for the cooking classes that were scheduled: exquisitely sharp knives, heat-resistant rubber spatulas, wooden juicers, peelers....

"Ponce," he explained, "we're trying to get to Santa Cruz by nine o'clock so I can see my homeopath who is going to help me not stress so much."

Having to get to an appointment on-time to help you stress *less* was becoming quite stress *full*.

Chapter Forty Nine

"Ponce!" dear Edward burst out, addressing himself to the only other creature awake in the house, "we're not going to make it. I'll never be ready, ever, let alone in time to get to my appointment." Ponce knew that this was a blatant fabrication as Edward did not get to be sixty-six by never, ever, getting things done. But he also knew that his Edward-ness did not take readily to receiving directives from others telling him to "calm down," "relax," "it's okay," "don't worry" (what did they know?) And no one was bopping Ponce on the head so that he could squeak out any advice that he might have anyway. All he could do was to love with all his heart, even though Edward did not seem to notice.

Still there was more to do, as Edward needed to pack up items for his Bazaar, as Edward was not just Zen teacher Edward or Zen cook Edward, he was also peddler Edward (Pedward), as it was another way to pay the bills: Give people an opportunity to shop. While his students were getting enlightened, their wallets could also become lighter (and you could buy now, pay later on the honor system—leaving an IOU with your name and contact information.)

Once upon a time Edward had been an entrepreneur with a boutique, but even before the world's economic fiascos became public knowledge, he had come down in standing; he was an itinerant without a location at a fashionable address—so let's talk straight here—he was a peddler. Starting off, he sold his cookbooks, and then added very sharp Japanese knives for cutting vegetables—"invite samurai sword technology to make itself at home in your kitchen"—to his inventory.

Then he added other people's books that had been useful for him: *The Grief Recovery Handbook, A General Theory of Love, The Four Agreements, The Invitation,* and so many more *(Easy to Love, Difficult to Discipline; On Becoming An Alchemist)*! On and on. So now, for a week away which included two cooking classes, he would bring along two hefty boxes of books.

Forget being a teacher and a peddler—Edward was a mule! A stressed mule balking at his assigned task. What was that mule-handler thinking, to be loading him down like this?

Chapter Fifty

While in the midst of raging about being a mule, Edward stressed his way around the house getting together the books. Ponce remained quietly alert. Edward was clearly stewing his way into a melt-down, and Ponce could only watch as the scene unfolded.

If you were to have looked closely at his face, especially his eyes, you would have seen for yourself that Ponce was no spring chicken. He'd been around the block—more than once—and those eyes were wise from observing family dynamics and energy patterns. He'd had a unique position inside the family watching what went into the soup, yet not falling into it himself. Thank goodness for that. If he had fallen in, he would have gotten stewed!

He knew that when raising temperamental children, parents are advised to be the adult—otherwise no one in the room will be grown-up—and the turmoil is bound to escalate. During escalation the child can almost always out-do the parent at being a child—after all they are the experts at this. In order to out-baby the baby (or the child), the parents must make absolute fools of themselves, which is not becoming at all.

Nobody is a winner in this scenario, even though the parents still have bigger bodies, and the children still have smaller ones. And those with bigger bodies believe that since they are paying the rent, they are entitled to rant as well. Those with smaller bodies are left wondering what they did wrong, when their mistake was being smaller than those who were bigger, and having big needs for those giants to take care of them.

Unfortunately, it looked to Ponce as if Edward had few if any "being-the-parent" skills. He was quickly losing his ground, and as his roots down into the earth had been abandoned, his feet quickly disappeared, followed in short order by his legs, pelvis, torso, shoulders, and neck. Then his head had blown up like an enormous balloon before it popped. Watery goo was puddling as far as Ponce's eye could see. Things had gotten messy.

Would they be heading south for healing, or going nowhere fast? Ponce was hoping for the best, whatever that turned out to be.

Chapter Fifty One

Often when things got messy, poor Edward did not know what to do: Persevere through the goo? Abandon ship? Take a break? Reassess? "I used to be more capable," he thought, "of driving myself to work hard. Wasn't that what Zen was all about—following the schedule, doing the next thing? Now what?"

Flummoxed about what to do next, he moved this way and that until his beloved Margot appeared sleepy-eyed. Noticing the stickiness in the air of the room, she was not sleepy-eyed for long. "Edward," she ventured, pressing her hand against his chest to slow his forward momentum, "this will never do. You cannot be driving like this." Edward was quick to protest that he would be okay. He needed to see his homeopath, and it was difficult, nearly impossible, to get an appointment in any sort of a timely way, and he wasn't in Santa Cruz that often, so he better stick to the plan despite the stickiness.

The mule-work of getting everything into the car continued—why didn't he have any young eager devotees to help him out when he needed them? Apparently Zen teachers who puddled did not attract eager young devotees. Finally with everything else in place, he took Ponce and Hobbes out to their place in the passenger seat, along with a covered travel mug of coffee for the cup-holder.

At the door of the kitchen, the good-byes were tender, yet a bit charged. Margot warmly held Edward, "I love you so very much," she said, "and I'm not sure it is wise for you to be driving in this state." Only she didn't say she wasn't sure. What she said was that she didn't want him to drive in the state that he was in. She wished he would change his plans.

Edward had the car all packed. He'd driven in many states of disarray, resuming competence as needed, and he believed that he could do it once again.

Okay then, he said, I understand your concern. I'll drive safely.

It was ten after seven in the morning, and stay-at-home Edward headed out into the morning commute traffic.

Chapter Fifty Two

Edward was wearing a pink polo shirt along with his new tan shorts that had lots of pockets, where you could stash things and later not know where to find them. Yes, his maroon Velcro wallet might be in the left back pocket, but not *that* left back pocket. For now it was chilly, but he was guessing that mid-coast California would be toasty. With the car heater on, everyone felt quite comfortable, though the critters on the passenger seat were not staying upright—as Edward in his haste to get out of town had neglected to fasten them in with the seat belt, or prop them behind some water bottles. Ponce lay on his side, a bit morose, while guessing that Edward would straighten him up in due time. He was doing his best to be patient. With Edward's exemplary melt-down only minutes behind them, Ponce focused on dispassionately observing the situation, and in hopes of keeping the driver calm, he was not voicing his displeasures.

The white Acura that Edward was driving had been such a dependable vehicle, except in his dreams, where it often disappeared or was stolen. His car was *not* where he had left it. That, or when he went to drive the white herd of horses that was his sporty mode of transportation, he would find a burnt blackened hulk or a skeletal frame that had been stripped for parts. Still, when he was awake, the white Integra had been extremely reliable, and decent enough to break down in a timely fashion. Once the clutch went out a block from his friends' house in Davis—how convenient was that? And another time the radiator had blown just as he was parking his car with friends in Burlingame who were taking him to the airport. When he got back from his trip, his friends had had the car repaired and ready to go. Good friends! His car seemed to have a knack and a knowing for when it was reaching a place of refuge.

Almost every time he went to the car wash, the guys who worked there would ask him if he wanted to sell it. But even though they knew how hot and responsive it was, they didn't know its innermost secrets the way that Edward did. He wasn't selling, no way.

That was not how his white Acura would disappear for good in the for-real world.

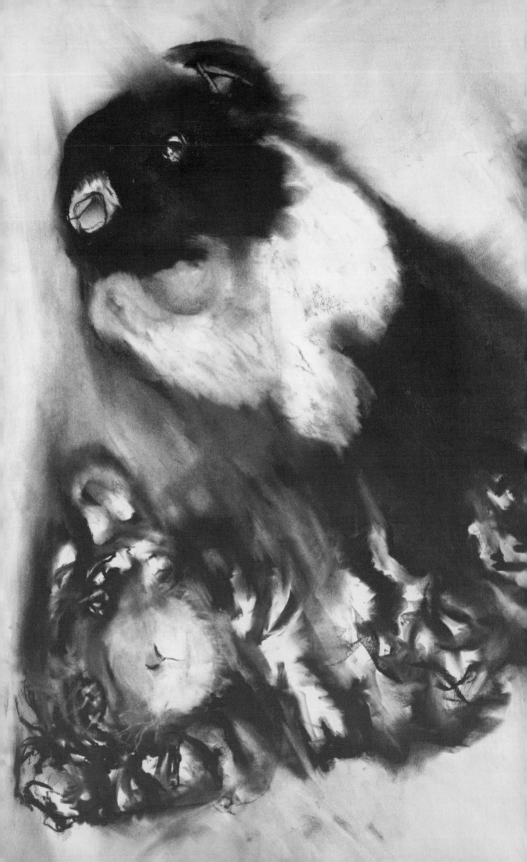

Chapter Fifty Three

As he was not able to see where he was going, while lying next to Hobbes who was curled-up beside him on the passenger seat, Ponce felt the stop and go of the car throughout his body. Lots of stop and go—first through Fairfax, then through San Anselmo, and San Rafael. A final right hand turn and then they were speeding up to enter the river of freeway traffic headed south toward San Francisco.

Pretty sweet—now they were really on their way, and everybody could relax, at least that was what Ponce was hoping: Let's breeze with ease, why don't we? Maybe he would get to meet Edward's homeopath in Santa Cruz. He could tell her a thing or two about Edward's symptoms after what he'd seen. Since he had only a squeaker and not much of a voice, he'd have to tell her with his deeply-expressive eyes. Ponce's heart went out to Edward for sure, but still and all, it had not been pretty watching him melt-down.

Ponce was not terribly familiar with the highway, so he could only guess where they were as they went over the hill to Greenbrae, along a level stretch passing Corte Madera, then up and down another hill to the exit and entrance for Mill Valley, his old homeland. Another flat stretch followed, flanked by frontage roads, and then they were passing the exit for Muir Woods and Muir Beach, the one they had taken to get to Green Gulch for Edward's lecture only a few days before.

Up the lengthy Waldo Grade, and about half way up they veered slightly to the right, lane by lane, so they were in the slower traffic. Shortly after that they were headed downhill, and as they entered the darkness Ponce could tell with an "A-ha!" that they must be in the Rainbow Tunnel.

Soon after that Ponce could not tell what was happening. A very slight left, a very slight right, and Ponce could hear the car scraping, and guessed with some apprehension that they had had a brief encounter with the right-hand guard rail. Then a sudden swing to the left, flashing through space and time, completely wild, and they were smashing, bouncing, rotating and spinning in a way that was not related to anyone's driving a car. A final crash, skid, and shudder, and Ponce, realizing that he'd closed his eyes, began to suspect that he could open them again. Where were they? What had happened?

Opening his eyes, Edward glanced down and saw what appeared to be his body: pink shirt, tan shorts, distant knees—there were probably feet down there somewhere. Glancing up, why, (of all things) there were the beige mountains west of the freeway—magnificent with brilliant blue above them! And turning his head, he discovered that the rear end of the car was butt-up against the middle freeway-divider.

"Guys," he said to the stuffies beside him, " I don't think we're going to Santa Cruz today."

Chapter Fifty Four

It was as though the fabric of the world had split open for a moment, and everything had come to a stop, complete and utter. Everything had happened so quickly. And nothing had happened—they were still alive and not obviously harmed—but somehow the weave seemed altered, the colors and patterns suggestive of other hands than usual.

Turning to look to his right, he saw a white pick-up truck stopped about four car lengths up the asphalt in the fast lane. Now that's a relief! Three lanes of morning commute traffic were streaming right to left before Edward's eyes—a ceaseless river of cars surging as full throttle as they could down the hill.

Feeling dismay at delaying the morning commute Edward thought to start up his car so he could re-enter the flow. His left foot moved to depress the clutch pedal, only to discover that it was not there. Was it the pedal or his foot? he wondered, and proceeded to check more consciously, putting his awareness into his leg, into his foot, assessing that they could move, then stepping for the clutch pedal. It was no use—"We're not going anywhere," he repeated, "there's no clutch pedal." Soon the authorities would be arriving.

A sneaky suspicion began to creep into Edward's awareness—that when the authorities arrived, as they surely would, they might not approve of the friends with whom he was conversing. And he didn't want those in power making disparaging comments: "So I guess the dumb bunny conversations of your stuffed animal friends had a screwy swerve to them," or, "I see your buddies here didn't exactly warn you of the dangers of driving distracted."

"What's this? A piggy and a tiger? You've got to be kidding. Were you focused on driving or on managing a fantasy camp for stuffies?" Edward knew they weren't going to Santa Cruz, and he didn't want to have to go into all that either: "But Officer, I can explain about the stuffed animals—and I'm really sorry that I didn't fasten their seat belt." Really.

So Edward did what a civilized grown-up would do—he put the stuffies into the back seat. "Guys, I'm really sorry to have to do this with you, but I don't know that under the circumstances I can afford to be associated with childish things such as yourselves. I'm feeling ashamed now that I'm not more of a grown-up who has out-grown stuffed animals and keeps his car on the straight and narrow."

What a betrayal that was for Ponce and Hobbes, to be scattered haphazardly onto the area of the back seat. Edward wasn't going to stand by them after all, after all their love and devotion to him! And after all his seeming love and devotion to them! When the rubber hit the road (and then the middle divider), they were being cast aside. Feeling devastated and bereft, they lay morosely, unmoving.

And the day was just beginning. It was barely past 7:30 in the morning. Where were they going, if they were not going to Santa Cruz?

Chapter Fifty Five

The driver of the white pick-up approached the passenger door. Edward struggled to remember how to open the window with the switch on his door, and couldn't find it—not in his mind, not in the car. There was such a thing somewhere, wasn't there? He leaned over to help as the man reached for the side door and opened it. "Are you okay, mate?" His voice was cheery yet concerned.

"Yes, I'm fine," attested Edward, who hadn't noticed any blood anywhere and had conducted a brief inventory of body parts to see if they were still connected to one another and capable of movement. "Fine, but I don't have a cell phone, so if you can call for help that would be great." "Right, mate, sure thing." And he was gone, leaving the passenger door wide open. In good hands, he was, mate.

A huge white tow truck was pulling up to his left—the bridge crew was there without even having to receive a call from his new-found mate—and the driver in off-white pants and a professional-looking thigh-length work coat sporting horizontal chartreuse reflector stripes strode toward the driver's door. This time Edward could find the power window button and press it, and in the background he could hear his mate up the hill saying, "It's okay, you don't need to send anyone. The bridge tow-truck is already here."

"Are you alright?" queried the approaching tow-truck driver. Edward once again testified that, "Yup, I'm fine, but I'm embarrassed about delaying the morning commute." "Oh, this is nothing," the man mused, "yesterday we had a ten-car crash in the tunnel. That was a mess to clean up." Edward thought to correct him, "I think that was Tuesday—and to-day is Thursday." Pausing to consider, his newest companion agreed, "Guess you're right. Listen, we'll have you out of here in no time, but we have to wait for the CHP before we move you. They'll be here within minutes."

The driver of the white pick-up truck reappeared, tossing a business card onto the passenger seat, "Call me later, and let me know you're okay, mate. I'm on my way."

Edward simply gushed with gratitude. The man had stopped his white truck in plenty of time, which meant others had not smashed into his car. He had checked on Edward's health and well-being.

"Thank you so much. Thank you so much." Edward was at a loss for words, so those would have to do. And his savior was gone.

Take it easy, then, self-soothed Edward, things will unfold step by step.

Chapter Fifty Six

Looking down, Edward observed that his pink shirt was laced with light brown coffee stains. Though artsy enough, this was rather baffling—wasn't the coffee in the cup in the cup-holder? Not really. Not at this moment. He reconnoitered and discovered the travel mug in his left hand. What it was doing there he could not recall, but there it was!

During the accident it must have been spray-painting his shirt out the little hole in the black plastic top. It was a genuine performance piece—coffee mug unconsciously decorates pink shirt—but probably not museum-worthy. Things were not quite congruent—and it took a great deal of concerted effort to move the mug left hand to right hand, right hand to cup-holder.

Still waiting for the authorities, Edward decided to get out of the car to stretch. First he unfastened his seat belt and reached over the passenger seat, now devoid of stuffies, to close the passenger door. Then he opened the driver's door and studied how to stand up, fairly confident that it would come back to him if he focused on connecting mind and body in something approaching the usual fashion: sending a mental signal... picturing action...movement occurring. He was out of the door standing in the morning chill. Well done, he congratulated himself.

Closing the driver's door was the next activity to dream up and execute. Edward believed that he was being so very careful and concentrated, until a sudden rushing of intense pain rocketed up his right arm. Then he could see that sure

enough his index finger was wedged between the door and
the frame, with his hand palm down on the white side of the
car. Pulling on his right arm, Edward found that his finger
slipped around and out of the corners of the compressed
space without his having to open the door. Blood was oozing
out of the finger pad that had popped open. He was injured.

Standing in the chill of the morning, Edward's body began to
tremble, especially his legs, uncontrollably. Sure the air was
cold, but Edward guessed that it was also his body's response
to trauma.

Shaking it off. Releasing the fight or flight impulses that
had frozen and not had the opportunity to move into action
during the accident.

Chapter Fifty Seven

A California Highway Patrolman appeared, coming from around the side of the tow truck, his sturdy presence in the familiar tan-uniform reassuring: "You okay? You're not injured?" "I'm fine, thank you." "That's good," he enthused, "metal and plastic can be replaced." At this point Edward's finger was numb with cold more than it was throbbing with pain.

"So," the officer continued, "there's something we need to talk about. You didn't hit anybody. Nobody hit you. There are no injuries. The only damage is to your car, and we call that *collision*. Your insurance will pay something for that if you're covered for it." Yes, I'm covered, Edward interjected.

"Now, you have to decide," the patrolman informed him, "if you want us to make an accident report. Because there is no damage except collision—and there are no injuries—we do not have to make an accident report, but we can, if you want to. If you do make an accident report, it will be a point on your record, and your insurance rates could go up. So would you like to make an accident report?" Edward could not imagine why he would want his insurance rates to go up, and was having difficulty grasping that no accident report was necessary: "Okay, well, if we don't have to, let's not."

Business out of the way, the officer was curious, "So what happened?"

Chapter Fifty Eight

Edward began to recount that he'd been driving in the far
right lane, and since the freeway entrance coming up the hill
from Sausalito was approaching, he had decided to move one
lane over to the left. He had started turning the wheel slightly
in that direction, and glancing back over his left shoulder, he
perceived that a big black pick-up truck was intently aiming
for that same spot on the freeway. So he'd thought, fine, he'd
stay in the right lane after all.

Except that when he looked straight ahead again, the white
Acura was bouncing once, than a second time on the con-
crete siding to the freeway. (How had he overshot the right
hand lane? –About three months later on that same stretch
of freeway, he finally realized that he had probably hit the
wall where the roadway was making a bend to the left, and
he'd probably gone a little too straight when returning to the
right lane.)

Though the car was pretty much on the roadway now, the
thought came to get a little further away from the side of the
road to avoid any more scraping. And Edward had turned
the wheel to the left –in fact way too far to the left, and the
car had responded. Feeling the pull of that left hand turn at
sixty-five miles an hour, Edward's mind had flashed: There's
nothing I can do about this now. We'll see where it ends up,
picturing, if anything, a bashing and battering of high-speed
metal, and a hospital room somewhere.

And then he'd opened his eyes to find himself here facing
west, directly away from the middle divider.

The CHP officer was nodding, saying, "Got it," and, "Pretty
lucky. We'll be moving your car off to the side of the freeway
and a local towing company will take it from there."

Chapter Fifty Nine

Edward stood there in the cold, a place of asphalt refuge from the nearby river of traffic, which seemed dark blue, speckled with dots of color. Another CHP officer appeared, this one younger, solicitous, "So, you're okay, are you?"

After assuring him that he was indeed okay, Edward then lifted his right index finger, showing off the spots of blood, and musing that ironically, this was probably his most painful injury, and that he had inflicted it on himself when he closed the car door after he'd stepped out onto the freeway.

The young officer suggested that he probably had a bandaid in his car—"Would you like one?" he asked Edward. "Sure, that would be great."

Then the first patrolman was back, observing that Edward looked rather cold, and suggesting he go sit in the warm patrol car parked up the roadway in the fast lane.

Sure enough the patrol car was quite cozy, the seat cushioned, the windshield clean enabling spacious viewing. A computer sat mounted between his passenger seat and the driver's. His bandaid arrived; his finger was bandaged. He wasn't on his way to Santa Cruz and San Luis Obispo, instead he was sitting curiously alive and well in a well-heated CHP patrol car, parked in the fast lane. Great view of the bridge! Edward mused, but he wasn't really looking.

Everyone really wanted to see him through this detour in his life.

Chapter Sixty

Mysteriously all three lanes of traffic had stopped, and Edward realized that the CHP officer had faced them to a standstill, and while one hand held them in check, he was gesturing to the tow-truck driver to cross the open highway to the right-hand dirt pull-out, Edward's white Acura in tow.

When the patrolman stepped aside, the river flowed onward. Then he was getting into the patrol car– professional, courteous, matter-of-fact—a man being of service, getting it done without any extra bother, *handling* the situation. And they maneuvered through three lanes of traffic to the far side of the roadway, pulling to a stop behind the tow truck.

"Do you know what you want to do? Can I give you a ride somewhere?" It was seven-fifty in the morning. "You might want to make some plans." Edward's response was not very practical, "I could go to the junkyard with the tow truck driver." "And then you would be stuck there without a vehicle." That was pretty obvious once it had been pointed out.

"Well, I could call my partner at home, and see if I could use her car. She teaches school in Mill Valley, and she doesn't usually leave for school until about eight."

"Do you have a cell phone?" the officer was asking, and when Edward shrugged that he didn't, the man produced an iPhone, and said, "Here, use mine. Dial the number and press the green button."

Sitting in the CHP vehicle, Edward pressed one number after another for his home phone. Margot answered. "Hello, it's Edward. I'm okay, but my car is gone. The CHP says that he could drive me to your school. I'm wondering if I could use your car today to go by the junkyard and empty all the stuff out of my car. Then I could pick you up at the end of the day."

Bereavements. Agreement.

Chapter Sixty One

Edward climbed out of the black and white CHP car and reconnoitered his way across the red-brown dirt to the tan-uniformed officer to return his iPhone, "She says that I can use her car, so you can take me to her school in Mill Valley, if it's not too much of a bother." Edward was feeling shaky and lost.

Again, the man was eminently reassuring. "No bother at all." "It's not out of your way?" "Not out of my way in the slightest."

"So before we get started, get whatever you want out of your car, whatever you think you might want before your car goes to the junkyard." That gave Edward pause, as he began to wonder if it was time to reclaim Ponce and Hobbes from the rest of the clutter in the backseat, which was not actually the backseat. With the back of the back seats flipped forward, it was one large cargo space back there.

The stuffies refused to meet Edward's glance towards them. Having been rejected. they continued to pout. "Guys," Edward whispered, "I promise with all my heart to pick you up at the junkyard. I'll be there as soon as I can. Promise." Then he grabbed his computer in its dark blue canvas bag. That was a grown-up thing to be taking with him. But it didn't do anything in the slightest to comfort the huge chasm inside, where there was not a sign of family, friends, sweethearts, or stuffies.

Growing up meant you were competent and stayed out of trouble. Then maybe your mother would not go away, and you could keep your stuffies. When you hit the wall, who or what would see you through?

That was the question.

Chapter Sixty Two

The patrol car made an immediate right hand turn heading directly off the edge of the dirt pull-out, which was a bit startling until an unpaved driveway appeared that sloped steeply down the side of the hill to merge with the freeway exit. They were on their way to Margot's school in Mill Valley.

The officer's vehicle was pleasantly warm, and felt quite reliable—solid and enduring. Through the underpass below the freeway, looping around to the right and up hill and onto the freeway: cruising. Cruising with power to spare, with power at his service, giving him a ride where he wanted to go.

His benefactor drove comfortably at ease, as Edward commented on the computer ("Yes, it's really been useful for us.") and then asked him how long he'd been with the CHP, "Oh, sixteen, seventeen years." "And all here?" "No, here in Marin, for two, three years so far. You can make requests for transfers as you acquire seniority."

Shortly after reaching the bottom of the hill, they were exiting for Stinson Beach and Muir Woods. All in a day's work, the officer could have been saying. And probably beings were this courteous beyond the grave as well—getting you where you needed to go.

How would you manage otherwise? When you had no vehicle?

Chapter Sixty Three

Still lying forlorn amongst the cardboard boxes of books and the cloth bags of cloths, Ponce and Hobbes felt the front of the car lifting, and they rolled slightly backwards. They'd been in a wreck, and now they were part of it. And what happens to wrecks? You get hauled off to the junkyard. Maybe there were dogs there, who prowled for prey. Maybe there was one of those giant machines that squished a big car top and bottom, smashed both sides inward, mashed the front and back together, and they would be locked forever in metal debris. You just didn't know. But imaginations could go anywhere, even more places than the internet.

The tow truck was moving forward, and they were on their way. There was a long silence as neither one knew what to say. Hobbes spoke first, "Ponce, my dear friend," and before he got any further the black-and-white piggy burst into tears. Simply hearing the tenderness in the tiger's voice had opened the well-springs, and Ponce's grief gushed out: "Just when I finally found a new home with all of you after all those years in boxes!"

"Yes for sure," Hobbes spoke to the air in front of his face, wishing that he could turn to face his friend and give him a hug of reassurance, "this is terribly distressing -- to be abandoned and sent off to the junkyard." Ponce's sobbing launched into another crescendo. Hobbes paused attentively to listen a bit, and then he added something of a cheer, "Cry for me too, Ponce!" The volume lifted and then as it was again diminishing, Hobbes resumed speaking, "Ponce, my dear friend, I am so happy to have met you again, and become friends as we have. You'll always have a place in my heart." Ponce sniffled that it had been just a few days! And now they were headed for junkyard oblivion.

Hobbes's conversation veered off in another direction entirely, "Ponce, do you suppose that there are other lives after this one?"

Chapter Sixty Four

Ponce paused in mid-sniffle to consider. Even though his eyes would not close, he closed them anyway, giving his attention to the space inside. Putting his attention there, he couldn't find a "before" or an "after."

He found his heart swelling even though nothing changed outwardly. The space within was like that: vast and expansive, warm and tender without dimensions. And all of his friends were gathering just as fast as he could think of them: Pomme and Margot, the fuzzy bunny, the giant white ape, porpoises, whales, and penguins.

There was Hobbes the unashamedly good-natured tiger, Zimt the companionable cinnamon bear, Ozzie the koala from Down Under, Binky the squeaky little bunny who answered to, "Hey, Bink, what do you think?" Turtle, the white and black cat, walked this way and that making sure there were no rodents on the loose. And there was Edward –he hadn't gone anywhere! He was right there inside with his arms reaching out to Ponce, his eyes smiling. Light was streaming from them, all up and down Ponce's spine, which was nowhere to be found, as stuffies don't have spines and Ponce was no exception.

A burst of astonishment flashed through Ponce. Left without any capacity for thinking about what was happening, he was one with everything, and everything was part of him. No separation could be found. Dazzling! What was there to think about? Nothing needed figuring out, and words felt so inadequate for capturing reality –"the black dragon jewel that you've been searching for is everywhere!" And that was nowhere at all. Ponce was in the center of the sparkle. And there was no Ponce to be found. Just sparkle, throughout space and time.

Hobbes's voice cut through his bliss, inquiring, "Hey Ponce, are you okay, my friend? You're not saying anything."

ILLUSTRATION BY JOHN SIMPKINS

Chapter Sixty Five

Okay? Was he okay? Given his altered state, how would he
know one way or another? Morning light was streaming in
the windows illuminating the particles of dust dancing in the
air, the car with its front end up was rolling along with some
unexpected bounces now and again.

Ponce felt his friend Hobbes's warm presence wash through
him. "Hobbes," he said, "you're the best!"

To which Hobbes replied, "We're all doing the best we can,
my friend, the very best we can."

Chapter Sixty Six

So much for road adventures, so much for awakenings, Ponce and Hobbes had ended up at the junkyard, abandoned by their beloved Edward. Sprawled in the back of the white Acura Integra, they waited. Though the day was sunny, the morning still felt chilly. The ghosts of all the nearby wrecks wafted through: shattered dreams, aborted missions, twisted plans, all come to an eerie silence.

Seconds unwound from the spool of timelessness, sometimes ticking, sometimes flowing. Nothing moved until the door opened, and there was Edward. Reaching out for the stuffies, he was apologizing again for having left them in the lurch.

Ponce and Hobbes felt themselves being picked up and held close to his face: "eddiebear!" they squealed, "eddiebear, take us home."

"By all means."

Edward Brown

Edward Brown began practicing Zen with Shunryu Suzuki Roshi in 1965, and received Dharma Transmission from Sojun Mel Weitsman in 1996. Known for his Tassajara cookbooks, he is also featured in Doris Doerrie's movie: How to Cook Your Life. Founder and teacher of the Peaceful Sea Sangha, he is old enough to know better.

Margot Koch

Margot Koch is a painter and art teacher,
special educator, co-founder of REAL School
Marin and proud mother of a son.
She lives in Marin County, California
with her partner, Edward
and didn't just fall off the cabbage truck.

COLOPHON

TYPOGRAPHY
ITC Legacy Sans and Serif by Ronald Arnholm

PAPER
Anthem Plus, 100lb text

PRINTING AND BINDING
McNaughton & Gunn, Saline, Michigan

DESIGN
Ingalls Design, San Francisco
Tom Ingalls and Kseniya Makarova

CHARCOAL DRAWINGS
Margot Koch

COLOR ILLUMINATION
John Simpkins

PHOTOGRAPHY
Edward Brown and Margot Koch

OTHER TITLES AND
UPCOMING PUBLICATIONS

Found Dharma Talks, Genine Lentine
49 Fingers, Michael Wenger
my-ness, Jane Hirshfield

ALSO BY EDWARD ESPE BROWN

The Tassajara Bread Book
Tassajara Cooking
The Tassajara Recipe Book
Tomato Blessings Radish Teachings
The Complete Tassajara Cookbook
co-author of the *Green's Cookbook*
editor of *Not Always So* – lectures by
    Shunryu Suzuki Roshi

www.peacefulseasangha.com

MISSING
LINKS
PRESS